Tell Me a Joke

Tell Me a Joke

...

edited by
Dana Bruce

...

illustrated by
Bill Sokol

...

Platt and Munk, Publishers, New York

Library of Congress Catalog Card No.: 66-10132

Guide on Safari:

"Now remember what I told you; when you see that leopard, shoot him on the spot."

Gamehunter:

"Which spot?"

Wife (eyeing fish on platter):
"Maggie, did you wash the fish before baking it?"

Maid:
"No ma'am. Why wash a fish that's lived all its life in water?"

First Patient:
"Is your dentist careful?"

Second Patient:
"Sure, he filled my teeth with great pains."

Joe:
"How much of that cheese did you eat?"

Willie:
"The hole of it."

Employer:
"You're an hour late. You should have been here at 9 o'clock."

Office boy:
"Why, what happened?"

Banker:
"How did you lose your hair?"

Bald Man:
"Worry."

Banker:
"About what?"

Bald Man:
"Losing my hair."

Willie:

"Lend me $50."

Joe:

"I only have $40."

Willie:

"Well then let me have the $40 and you can owe me $10."

Mother:

"What's the difference between a head of cabbage and a lemon?"

Mary:

"I don't know."

Mother:

"I'd hate to send you to the store for a head of cabbage."

Passenger:
"When the train stops will you please tell me at which end to get off?"

Conductor:
"It doesn't matter, lady, both ends stop."

Optometrist:
"There now, with glasses you'll be able to read everything."

Little Boy:
"You mean I really don't have to go to school anymore?"

Little boy:
"You must live in an apartment with very low ceilings."

Lady:
"Why do you say that, Sonny?"

Little boy:
"Your dog wags its tail side to side instead of up and down."

Swimming Instructor:

"Now girls, swimming is the best exercise for keeping you slim and beautiful. It's really good for the figure."

Pupil:

"Did you ever look at a duck?"

Tom:
"Do you know how to write?"

Bill:
"Sure, but I never write."

Tom:
"Why not?"

Bill:
"I don't know how to read."

Customer:
"I can't pay for this suit for three months."

Tailor:
"That's all right."

Customer:
"When will it be ready?"

Tailor:
"In three months, sir."

Cousin Tom:
"Where's the other windmill gone, Uncle?"

Farmer Brown:
"We only had wind enough for one, so we took the other down."

Judge:
"I'll give you ten days or $50."

Prisoner:
"I'll take the $50, judge."

Gentleman:

"Waiter, this meat is bad!"

Waiter:

"Who told you, sir?"

Gentleman:

"A little swallow."

Man:

"What's the quickest way to get to the hospital?"

Little Boy:

"Just close your eyes and start across the street. You'll be there in a few minutes."

Farmer: (hailing car):

"If you're going into town, John, will you take my shoes along with you?"

John:

"Sure. Where do you want me to leave them?"

Farmer:

"Don't worry about that. I'll be in them."

Older sister:
"Why are you wearing my new raincoat?"

Younger sister:
"I didn't want your new dress to get wet."

Salesman:
"This machine is really worth having. It will do half your work."

Clerk:
"In that case, I'll take two."

Plumber:

"Mrs. Brown, I'm the plumber."

Mrs. Brown:

"But I didn't send for the plumber."

Plumber:

"I know, but the people downstairs did."

Lady Tourist:

"What's this necklace made of?"

Indian:

"Crocodile teeth."

Lady Tourist:

"I suppose they mean the same thing to you as pearls do to us?"

Indian:

"Not quite, madam. It's easy to open an oyster."

Old Man:

"Fine looking baby! How old is he?

Little Girl:

"He'll be one next week."

Old Man:

"He sure doesn't look that old."

Little Girl:

"Well, he was very young when he was born."

Pupil:
"What has 12 legs, a brown fuzzy body, and purple eyes?"

Teacher:
"I don't know, what has?"

Pupil:
"I don't know either, but it certainly doesn't look nice on your neck."

Patient:
"I can't sleep these nights, doctor. I have terrible insomnia. What shall I do?"

Doctor:
"Sleep near the edge of the bed. You'll probably drop off more easily."

The judge looked at the prisoner and thought he'd seen him in court before.

"Have you ever been up before me?" asked the judge.

"I don't think so," the man said. "I work nights and don't get up till three in the afternoon."

Doctor:

"Your cough sounds much better this morning."

Patient:

"It should. I've been practicing all night."

Ivensky:

"My grandfather was a Pole."

Woody:

"North or South?"

Customer:

"I ordered blueberry pie, waiter. This looks like pumpkin pie to me."

Waiter:

"What does it taste like?"

Customer:

"I don't really know."

Waiter:

"If you can't tell the difference, it doesn't really matter, does it?"

Circus Performer:

"The circus hired me to put my head in the lion's mouth."

Willie:

"Isn't that hard on the lion?

Circus Performer:

"Oh no, his part of the act is a snap."

Wife (to maid):

"Have you given the goldfish any water lately?"

Maid:

"No, ma'am, they haven't finished the water I gave them last month."

Joe:

"I saw a man-eating shark at the aquarium."

Willie:

"That's nothing, I saw a man eating herring in the restaurant."

Tourist:

"What kind of fish are these?

Lifeguard:

"Jellyfish."

Tourist:

"What flavor?"

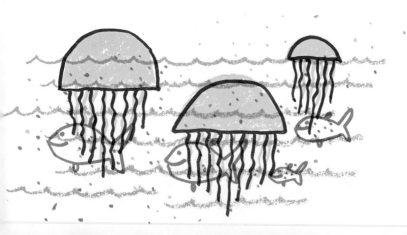

Mother:
"Johnny, finish your alphabet soup."
Johnny:
"No thanks, mom, not another word."

"Are you and your twin sister the oldest in the family?"
"Oh no, mom and dad are much older."

Vagrant: (knocking at farmer's door):
"Good day, ma'am. Can you help me out?"

Farmer's Wife:
"Would you like a nice chop for supper?"

Vagrant:
"What is it? Pork, lamb, or wood?"

1st Baseball Fan:
"I can tell the score before the game starts."

2nd Baseball Fan:
"You can! What it is?"

1st Baseball Fan:
"Nothing to nothing."

"I've got to find the candy I dropped," said Mr. Brown, searching under the table.
"Never mind, dear," said his wife, "Take another one."
"I've got to find that one," her husband replied. "My teeth are in it."

Barry:
"My brother swallowed a firecracker last night."

Harry:
"Is he all right?"

Barry:
"I don't know. I haven't heard the last report."

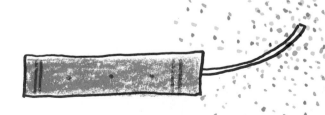

Wife:
"Henry, wake up."

Henry:
"What's wrong."

Wife:
"I heard a mouse squeak."

Henry:
"What do you want me to do, get up and oil it?"

First Pelican:
"Pretty good fish you have there."

Second Pelican:
"Well, it fills the bill."

Man (finding a rabbit in his refrigerator):
"What are you doing here?"

Rabbit:
"It says 'Westinghouse' on the outside of this icebox, doesn't it? Well, I'm westing."

Gentleman:

"Didn't I meet you in St. Louis?"

Stranger:

"No, I was never in St. Louis."

Gentleman:

"Neither was I. It must have been two other fellows."

Mother:

"Tommy, I thought you were going to practice playing that duet on the piano with your sister?"

Tommy:

"I did, Mom. I've already finished my part."

Hostess:

"Won't you have something more, Billy?"

Billy:

"No thanks, I'm full."

Hostess:

"Well, then, put some fruit and candies in your pocket to eat on the way home."

Billy:

"No thanks, they're full too."

"I've only one eye, so of course I only see half the show. Don't you think you could let me in for half price?" asked the one-eyed man at the cashier's office.

"It'll take you twice as long to see the whole show, so you'll have to pay double," replied the cashier.

Teacher:
"Johnny, how far away were you from the right answer to that sum?"

Johnny:
"Only two seats away, teacher."

Employer:
"Why is your grammar so rusty?"

Secretary:
"I left my typewriter in the rain."

Actor:

"They wanted to put me on after the monkey act, but I refused."

Willie:

"Why, were you afraid the audience would think it was an encore?"

First Hunter:

"What are you doing with that rifle?"

Second Hunter:

"Hunting for moose."

First Hunter:

"There are no moose around here."

Second Hunter:

"I know. If there were, I wouldn't have to hunt for them."

Druggist:

"Did you kill the moths with those mothballs I recommended?"

Customer:

"No, I sat up all night throwing them at the moths, but I couldn't hit a single one."

Hunter:

"I went lion hunting with a club."

Willie:

"With just a club? Weren't you afraid."

Hunter:

"No, there were over one hundred members in the club."

Diner:

"This lobster only has one claw."

Waiter:

"I'm sorry sir, the lobster got into a fight with another lobster and that's how he lost his claw.

Diner:

"Then take him back and bring me the winner."

Servant:

"The doctor has come, Professor."

Professor:

"Oh dear, I just can't see him now. Tell him I'm ill."

Professor:

"Why are you so late?"

Student:

"Class started before I got here."

Teacher:

"What is the highest form of animal life?"

Pupil:

"The giraffe."

Joe:

"I bought a goat this morning."

Mother:

"Where are you going to keep him?"

Joe:

"In the house."

Mother:

"What about the smell?"

Joe:

"He won't mind that."

Doctor:

"I think you need a good rest."

Woman Patient:

"But doctor, I think I need some medicine. Why don't you look at my tongue?"

Doctor:

"I don't have to. I'm sure it could use a good rest too."

Grandfather:
"So you're going to school now! What will you be when you graduate?"

Davie:
"Old, I think."

Willie:

"I do my hardest work before breakfast."

Joe:

"What's that?"

Willie:

"Getting up."

Diner:

"Is it customary to tip the waiter in this restaurant?"

Waiter:

"Yes, sir."

Diner:

"Then hand me a tip. I've already waited an hour for the steak I ordered."

Teacher:

"As we walk out on a cold winter day and look around, what do we see on every hand?"

Pupil:

"Gloves."

Teacher:

"What's cowhide used for?"

Pupil:

"For keeping cows together."

Old man:

"Does your watch tell the time, little girl?"

Little girl:

"No, you have to look at it."

"I've told thousands of people where to get off," bragged the timid little man.

"I don't believe you," said his friend.

"It's true," the little man replied, "I'm an elevator operator."

Mother:
"What are you drawing, Tommy?"

Tommy:
"A picture of Heaven."

Mother:
"But you can't do that. No one knows what Heaven looks like."

Tommy:
"Well, they will when I've finished the picture."

Passer-by:

"Good river for salmon."

Fisherman:

"Sure must be. I can't get any of them to leave it."

Joe:

"I discovered a way to rid my dog of fleas."

Willie:

"How?"

Joe:

"I take him up in an airplane, do a few stunts, and the fleas get scared and jump off."

Wife:

"What was all that hammering?"

Husband:

"I was just taking the screens off the windows to let the flies out."

Diner:

"I don't like the flies in the restaurant today."

Waiter:

"Well, come back tomorrow and we'll have some new ones."

The absent-minded professor on the subway was strap-hanging with one hand, and he carried a bundle of books in the other. He looked worried.

"Can I help you, sir?" asked a friendly traveler.

"Oh, thank you. Would you hold onto this strap while I get my fare out?"

Lady:
"I like this dog, but his legs are too short."

Owner of pet shop:
"Why, all four reach the ground, don't they?"

Customer:
"I don't like the looks of that codfish."

Grocer:
"If you want looks, lady, why don't you buy a goldfish?"

Teacher:
"Bobby, your essay on Our House is word for word the same as your sister's."

Bobby:
"Sure, teacher, it's the same house."

Davie:

"Dad, gimme a dime."

Dad:

"Davie, you're too old to be begging for dimes."

Davie:

"O.K. Dad, gimme a dollar."

"And what will you do when you grow up to be as big as mommy?"

"Diet."

Optometrist:

"So you have weak eyes? How many letters are on the first line of the chart?"

Client:

"What chart?"

Patient:

"Doctor, I've a pain in my left leg."

Doctor:

"There's nothing I can give you for it. It's old age."

Patient:

"But doctor, the right leg is just as old as the left one and it doesn't hurt at all."

First Lady:
"Just think, 3,000 seals were used to make fur coats last year."

Second Lady:
"Isn't it wonderful they can train animals to do such work!"

"When do you plan to open your bakery?"
"When I can raise the dough."

"What did you do when the ship sank?"
"Oh, I grabbed a cake of soap and washed
myself ashore."

Little Doris (saying her prayers):
"Please God, make San Francisco the capital
of Missouri."
Mother:
"Why, Doris, what made you say that?"
Little Doris:
"Because I said so in my examination paper
today, and I want it to be right."

"My sister has three feet."
"I don't believe you!"
"Then how come she wrote a letter saying
she'd grown three feet?"

Inventor:

"I invented a new kind of flea powder."

Friend:

"Does it kill fleas?"

Inventor:

"No, but it makes them itch."

Patient:

"Doctor, I'm worried about my diet. Do you think oysters are healthy?"

Doctor:

"I've never heard one complain."

Teacher:

"Susan, can you tell me what jam is?"

Susan:

"Jam is the stuff that makes bread and butter not taste so good when you don't put any on."

Vet:

"This cow must have a tablespoon of this medicine twice daily."

Farmer:

"But our cow doesn't use a tablespoon. She drinks out of a pail."

"I'm really in trouble!"
"What's wrong?"
"I've lost my glasses and I can't look for them
    until I've found them."

John:

"How did you find the weather when you were on vacation?

Jim:

"Just went outside and there it was."

"Which is the other side of the street?"
"Over there."
"That's strange, the gentleman over there said it was over here."

Diner:

"Waiter, there's a bug in my tea cup. What does this mean?"

Waiter:

"How should I know. If you want your fortune told, go see a gypsy."

Driver:

"I just smashed my car up. I was out driving and I hit a cow."

Friend:

"A Jersey cow?"

Driver:

"I don't know. I didn't see the license plate."

Teacher:

"Why does cream cost more than milk?"

Mary:

"Because it's harder for the cows to sit on the small bottles."

Teacher:

"Name five things that contain milk."

Pupil:

"Ice cream, butter, cheese, and two cows."

Little Jimmy:
"How can you eat soup with a moustache?"

Uncle Joe:
"It's quite a strain!"

"Are you a good student?"
"Yes and no."
"What does that mean?"
"Yes, I am no good."

American:

"The poor man was killed by a revolving crane."

Englishman:

"My, what fierce birds you have in America."

"Why does a polar bear wear a fur coat?"
"Because he'd look funny in a woolen one."

Customer:

"I thought you said this dog was a good watchdog."

Pet Shop Owner:

"Well, isn't he?"

Customer:

"Certainly not. Last night he barked so loud that the burglars came and went without our hearing them."

Mr. Smith:

"I used to be in politics myself. I was dog-catcher in my town for two years, but finally I lost the job."

Mr. Jones:

"What happened?"

Mr. Smith:

"I finally caught the dog."

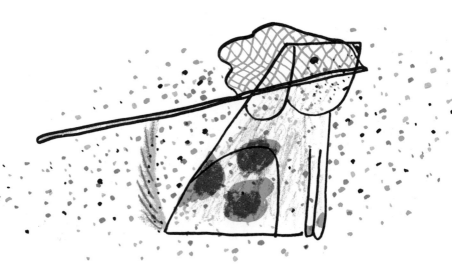

Angry Lady:

"Call your dog off."

Willie:

"I can't. I've called him Fido ever since he was a pup, and it's too late to change his name now."

Gentleman:

"Doorman, call me a cab."

Doorman:

"You're a cab."

First Bum:

"I'm looking for a job. Have you heard of any?"

Second Bum:

"I think they need a man over at the Eagle Laundry."

First Bum:

"Aw, I never had any practice washing eagles."

Mr. Jones:

"I used to know Mr. Smith, who was with your firm. I understand he was a tried and trusted employee—"

Banker:

"He was trusted, yes, and he will be tried if we ever catch him."

Teacher:

"Did any of you children ever see an elephant's skin?"

Willie:

"I did, teacher."

Teacher:

"Where was it?"

Willie:

"On an elephant."

Father:

"Well, what did you learn in Sunday school today?"

Son:

"We learned all about a cross-eyed bear."

Father:

"A what?"

Son:

"Yes sir, a bear named Gladly. We learned a song about him. 'Gladly the cross I'd bear.'"

Teacher:

"Mary, can you make up a sentence with the phrase 'bitter end' in it?"

Mary:

"How about, 'Our dog chased our cat, and he bitter end.'"

Teacher:

"Jones, spell 'weather.'"

Jones:

"W-e-t-t-h-e-r."

Teacher:

"Well, that's certainly the worst spell of weather we've had in a long time."

Landlady:

"I'll give you three days in which to pay your rent."

Student:

"O.K., I'll pick the Fourth of July, Christmas and Easter."

"So you say that you can tell me everything that's in your dictionary!" said the teacher in surprise.

"Of course I can," said Fred, "There's ma's pressed rose leaves, three old snapshots, a few postcards and a pawn check for pa's trombone."

First Traveler:

"I spent last summer in a very pretty city in Switzerland."

Second Traveler:

"Berne?"

First Traveler:

"No, I almost froze."

Farmer:

"Come into the barn, sonny, and I'll show" you how to milk a cow."

City boy:

"Don't you think I'd better start on a calf?"

Father:
"How many letters in the alphabet?"

Son:
"I don't know."

Father:
"You've been to school for four years and you don't know how many letters there are in the alphabet?"

Son:
"Well, you've been to the post office and you don't know how many letters are there!"

Customer:
"What's this?"

Waiter:
"That's bean soup, sir."

Customer:
"I'm not interested in what it's been—I'm asking what it is now."